Contents

Introduction

Shakespeare

William Shakespeare was born in Stratford-upon-Avon in 1564. He is the most famous writer of plays in the English language, so it is perhaps surprising that we really know very little about his life. He probably went to the grammar school in Stratford, and so it is likely that he had a good education, especially in Latin.

The next thing we know is that he married Anne Hathaway in 1582, and they had three children: Suzanna (born in 1583), and a boy and a girl (Hamnet and Judith) born at the same time in 1585.

After that, we know nothing until 1592, when he was already writing successful plays in London. We don't know when he went there. By 1597, Shakespeare had made enough money as a writer and actor to buy New Place, the largest house in Stratford. He may have retired to New Place in 1610, but he continued to write plays. The last play he wrote was *Henry VIII*, in 1612. The company were performing that play at the Globe Theatre on 20 June 1613 when the theatre was burnt to the ground.

Shakespeare died at Stratford on 23 April 1616.

Comedies and tragedies

This book contains the stories of four of Shakespeare's plays: two comedies and two tragedies.

Today, a *comedy* is a play in which the story and the people are amusing, and which ends happily. In Shake-

LONGMAN CLASSICS

Stories
from
Shakespeare

Simplified by Brian Heaton
and Michael West

Longman

Longman Group UK Limited,
Longman House, Burnt Mill, Harlow,
Essex CM20 2JE, England
and Associated Companies throughout the world.

This simplified edition © Longman Group UK Limited 1987

First published 1987
Reprinted 1988

ISBN 0-582-52283-8

Set in 10/13 point Linotron 202 Versailles
Produced by Longman Group (FE) Limited
Printed in Hong Kong

Acknowledgements

'Photographs © BBC' 1971, for pages 21, 32 and 40; Donald
Cooper for pages 7, 12, 47 and 51; Zöe Dominic for page 24 and
the cover.

The cover background is a wallpaper design called NUAGE,
courtesy of Osborne and Little plc

Stage 3: 1300 word vocabulary

Please look under *New words* at the back of this book
for explanations of words outside this stage.

speare's time, a play with a happy ending was a comedy, but the happenings in the play needn't all be amusing, and the characters – the people – may be far from funny. The happy ending is for the characters we are expected to like.

The Merchant of Venice ends happily for Antonio (the merchant of Venice), his friend Bassanio, the beautiful and clever Portia, and their friends. So *The Merchant of Venice* is a comedy. The ending is not happy for Shylock, but the people who saw the play in Shakespeare's time (it was probably first played in 1598) wouldn't have liked Shylock and wouldn't have been sorry for him.

A Midsummer Night's Dream was written at about the same time as *The Merchant of Venice*. It is a comedy, but of a different kind. It ends happily for everybody, including the two pairs of lovers, the king and queen of the fairies, and even for Bottom, the funny clothmaker.

Most of us like a happy ending to a story or a play, but the playgoers of Shakespeare's time also liked to have their feelings moved by a tragedy. A *tragedy* is a serious play that ends sadly, especially one that ends with the death of the main character or characters.

The main character, for us, in *Hamlet* is Prince Hamlet of Denmark. By the end of the play, we are very sorry for him, but we don't feel that a happy ending would be right. He dies, and we are sad, but he has died well, and we feel that the ending is right.

Julius Caesar himself is the cause of almost everything that happens in the tragedy *Julius Caesar*, but he is not the character whose feelings we share. That character is Brutus. Even his enemy says about Brutus that "This was the noblest Roman of them all." He dies in the play, partly because that is what really happened in history (in 42 BC), partly because it is the only end that seems right.

Reading the stories

When we read the stories in this book, we must try to see the action and hear the spoken words in two ways. First, as they were in history; second, as they were played in the theatre in Shakespeare's time, with the actors wearing the clothes of Shakespeare's time.

Venice in the sixteenth century was a powerful Italian city-state. Its merchants traded with countries all round the Mediterranean Sea. Precious goods and materials from the south and east of Asia came to it by sea from the countries on the eastern coasts of the Mediterranean. The Venetian merchants sold them to traders from every part of Europe. The Duke (called the *Doge*) ruled with a Grand Council.

The city of *Athens* in ancient Greece was a less clear picture in the minds of Shakespeare and the British people of Queen Elizabeth I's time. Shakespeare didn't want the setting to be too clear. He knew, of course, that his Duke of Athens was a story-book hero (Theseus) from the days before history was written. In such a place in a far-away world he could bring in fairies, with their king and queen, and magic. And it was all fun if the people in his theatre seemed to find some very foolish "workmen from Athens" surprisingly like workmen of London in their own time.

Denmark in the tenth century was nearly as misty as ancient Greece, but some of the people in Shakespeare's theatre knew that parts of England had Danish rulers at that time.

The story of Julius Caesar, set in *Rome* and other places in Italy in the first century BC, is a matter of history, but Shakespeare was willing to change a few events to make a better play.

The Merchant of Venice

Antonio and Bassanio

A merchant called Antonio lived in Venice. Everyone in Venice liked Antonio because he was a good man. He had many ships which traded with other countries. At the time of our story, his ships were all at sea.

The friend whom Antonio loved the most was called Bassanio. When Bassanio's father died, he left his son a lot of money. But Bassanio soon spent it all; he became poor and very unhappy.

One day Bassanio told Antonio that he was in love with Portia, a rich and beautiful lady who lived at Belmont, near Venice. Portia's father left her all his money on his death, so she was very rich. Bassanio was sad because he could never ask Portia to marry him while he himself had no money. He knew that many rich young men were going to Belmont to try to marry Portia. So he asked Antonio to lend him three thousand ducats (the money of Venice at that time).

"I haven't any money just now," Antonio replied. "All my money and goods are at sea. I am waiting for my ships to return. Find someone who knows me and will lend money to me. Then I will get the money and lend it to you so that you can go to Belmont and marry Portia."

Shylock

Bassanio went to a man who lent money. The money lender's name was Shylock. Shylock had a lot of money, but he loved it too much. He used to lend his money to merchants and then make them pay back much more than they had borrowed. Therefore the merchants of Venice did not like Shylock. Antonio used to warn other merchants about Shylock.

Shylock had never liked Antonio.

"Antonio is kind and will lend his money to anyone," he said. "He never makes people pay him back more than they borrowed. He makes things difficult for me."

When Bassanio asked Shylock to lend him three thousand ducats for three months, Shylock knew that Antonio would soon be in his power!

"I shall never forgive Antonio," he said to himself. "I shall not be happy till I have caught him."

"You do not like the way I make my money," Shylock told Antonio when they met. "You have called me a dog and treated me like a dog. Now you come to me to ask for money. Does a dog have money? Can a dog lend a person three thousand ducats? Shall I bow to you and thank you for treating me like a dog? And shall I lend you money?"

But Antonio was not afraid.

"If you lend me money," he replied, "don't lend it to me as you would lend it to a friend. Lend it to me as you would lend it to an enemy. If I can't pay you back, you can make me suffer for it."

"I want to be your friend," said Shylock. "I shall forget what has happened in the past and lend you the money." Then he pretended to laugh. "Let us play a game: if you don't pay back the money at the end of three months," he said, "you must promise to give me a pound of your flesh; you must allow me to cut the flesh from your body."

Antonio laughed too and agreed to this: he did not think that Shylock really meant what he said. But Bassanio was afraid. He said, "I think Shylock will do what he says. I don't want you to get money from Shylock."

"Don't be afraid," said Antonio. "In two months my ships will return and bring me plenty of money."

So Antonio borrowed the money from Shylock and gave it to Bassanio.

The three boxes

Before he died, Portia's father thought of a way to find a good husband for his daughter. He thought, "I am afraid that many young men will want to marry Portia because she is rich. So I shall leave three small boxes – one box made of gold, another made of silver, and the third made of lead. The man who wants to marry Portia must choose the right box."

Portia and her servant Nerissa were talking about all the young men who had come to try to win Portia. A servant came into the room.

"A prince has come from Africa," he said.

Portia showed the prince all the boxes, and the prince carefully read everything that was written on each box.

On the gold box were the words: "The man who chooses me shall get what many men wish for."

On the silver box were the words: "The man who chooses me shall get as much as he ought to get."

And on the lead box were the words: "The man who chooses me must give, and must be ready to lose everything he has."

"My picture is inside the right box," said Portia. "Choose!"

The prince studied the words on all three boxes: he said, "All the world wishes for gold; all the world wishes for Portia, so I choose the gold box."

The prince took the key from Portia and opened the box. But he was surprised when all he saw inside was the head of a dead man and a piece of paper. On the paper was written: "All that shines brightly is not gold."

The prince left with a sad heart and Portia was pleased to see him go.

Bassanio visits Portia

Then a French prince came. He was very proud, so he chose the silver box: "The man who chooses me shall get as much as he ought to get." The proud prince said, "I am a great man: so I ought to get all that I wish for." He opened the box; in it he found a picture of a fool's head. There was also a piece of paper in the box. It said, "There are many fools covered in silver." The prince said, "I have been a fool!" and he went away.

A servant came to Portia and said, "A young man from Venice is coming to try to win you." This young man was, of course, Bassanio.

There were many servants with Bassanio. There was also a man called Gratiano. Gratiano was both a servant and a friend of Bassanio.

Portia had fallen in love with Bassanio. She said, "Please wait a day or two before you begin to choose; if you choose the wrong box, I shall see no more of you. I could teach you how to choose the right box, but I have promised not to do that."

Bassanio said, "No. Let me choose now. I can't bear to wait."

Bassanio chooses

Bassanio looked at the gold and silver boxes. He thought, "Those things which seem beautiful from the outside are

4

not always beautiful inside. The lead box does not promise to give me anything. It tells me that I should be ready to give all that I have to the woman whom I love. So I choose this."

He opened the lead box, and in it he saw Portia's picture. Then he read the paper which was in the box: "If you are pleased with this, turn to your lady and kiss her."

Bassanio turned to Portia and said, "Dear lady, will you be mine?"

"I wish," answered Portia, "that I were a thousand times more beautiful and ten thousand times richer; then I might be good enough for you. I give you myself, and all that is mine."

She took a ring off her finger and gave it to him.

"Take this ring," she said. "When you lose it, or give it away, that will be the end of our love."

"When this ring leaves my hand," answered Bassanio, "then life will have left me. I shall be dead."

As Portia and Bassanio stood talking about their love for each other, Gratiano and Nerissa came up to them. Nerissa said, "We wish you joy in your marriage. Gratiano and I are to be married, too."

A letter from Antonio

Just as the four happy people were arranging to be married, three friends arrived from Venice with a letter from Antonio. Bassanio opened the letter and began to read it.

Portia looked at Bassanio's face. She was sure that something very bad had happened. She said, "I am half of you, and I must have half of anything which troubles you. Tell me what it is."

Bassanio read the letter:

Dear Bassanio, My ships are all lost. Now I have no money, so I cannot pay Shylock. I must give him a pound of my flesh. If I do that, it will certainly be the end of my life. Therefore please forget about the money that you borrowed from me. All I wish now is to see you before I die.

The kind Portia told Bassanio to go at once to his friend. But she wanted Bassanio to marry her before he went. Then he would be able to take her money and pay Shylock. So as soon as they were married, Bassanio hurried off to Venice to see his dear friend, Antonio.

When Bassanio and Gratiano had gone, Portia thought of a way to save Antonio. She decided to go to Venice herself.

Portia had a good friend who was a famous judge. She asked him to lend her all his judge's clothes and notes. Then she put on the clothes and pretended to be a judge. Her maid, Nerissa, was dressed like a judge's manservant.

Then Portia and Nerissa set out for Venice.

Antonio in danger

Shylock was very angry with Antonio. One of Antonio's friends had run away with Shylock's beautiful daughter. They were in love with each other and they had run away to get married. They had also taken some of Shylock's money and jewels.

Shylock was so angry that he ran through the streets of Venice. He shouted to everyone about his daughter and the money that she had taken. All the little boys in Venice followed him and laughed at him.

"His jewels, his daughter, and his money," they shouted.

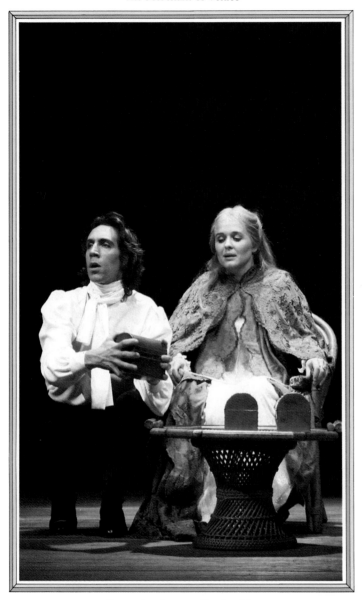

Bassanio chooses the lead box

When the angry Shylock heard that Antonio's ships were lost at sea, he was very pleased. He knew that now he could kill Antonio.

Antonio asked Shylock to give him another chance to pay. But Shylock would not listen to him.

"Guard him well," Shylock said to the man who was taking Antonio to prison. "Don't ask me to forgive him. Don't talk to me about mercy and forgiveness. I won't have mercy: I'll take my pound of flesh from him."

The brave Antonio did not again ask Shylock for mercy, for he knew that Shylock meant to kill him. All Antonio wished for now was to see his friend Bassanio once more.

The court

Antonio was taken to court, and the trial began. The Duke of Venice said to Shylock, "Have mercy on Antonio."

"I have been promised my pound of flesh," Shylock answered. "Antonio is my enemy: I hate him."

Bassanio said, "Do all men kill those things that they hate?"

"It is useless trying to talk to Shylock," said Antonio. "Don't wait any longer. Pass judgement on me and give Shylock what he wants."

"I'll pay you six thousand ducats in return for the three thousand ducats that Antonio borrowed," said Bassanio.

"If you offered me six times the amount that you have just offered," said Shylock, "I would still take my pound of flesh. Give me my pound of flesh!"

"How can you hope for mercy yourself when you show none?" asked the duke.

"I have done nothing wrong and I fear no judgement," Shylock replied. "Give me my pound of flesh!"

As the duke was wondering what to do, Portia entered

the large room, dressed like a judge. Bassanio did not know that it was Portia. Nerissa was with her, dressed like a young man.

Portia took her seat as judge.

"Are you Antonio? – And is this your agreement with Shylock?"

"It is."

"Then," said Portia, "Shylock must be merciful: he must have mercy on Antonio."

"Why must I have mercy on him?" said Shylock.

Portia answered:

"Mercy falls like the gentle rain from the sky upon the earth. It blesses him who gives it, and him who receives it. Kings have mercy in their hearts. And God has mercy: he had mercy upon us. We all pray to God for mercy: so we should learn to show mercy to others. Do you still ask for this pound of flesh?"

"I ask for what is mine by law!" answered Shylock.

"Oh, wise young judge!"

Bassanio said, "I offer ten times the amount of money that Antonio has borrowed. Please change the law a little so that we may save Antonio."

"We cannot change a law," answered Portia. "If one law is changed, then other men will later want to change other laws."

"Oh, wise young judge!" cried Shylock.

Portia said, "Let me see this agreement, this promise of Antonio to you."

"Here it is!" answered Shylock, giving her the paper.

"Yes," she said. "By law Shylock may have a pound of flesh to be cut off by him nearest to Antonio's heart. Be merciful! Let me destroy this paper. – No? Then, Antonio, be ready; and Shylock, take your knife."

"Oh, learned judge! Oh, wise young man!" cried Shylock.

"Have you brought anything to weigh the flesh?" Portia asked Shylock.

"Yes," answered Shylock. "I have everything ready here."

"Do you wish to say anything?" Portia asked Antonio.

"Only a little," replied the brave Antonio. "Goodbye, Bassanio. Don't be sad for me. Tell your wife about me and how much I loved you. If Shylock cuts deep enough, I'll pay him back with all my heart."

"I love you more than my own life, more than my wife, and more than all the world," cried Bassanio. "I would gladly lose everything in order to save you."

"Your wife wouldn't like that offer if she were present," said Portia.

Then Gratiano, who liked to do everything that Bassanio did, spoke about his own wife.

"I have a wife, whom I love very much," he said. "But I wish that she were dead and in heaven. Then she would be able to ask God to help Antonio."

Nerissa laughed quietly when she heard her husband.

"It is good that you make this wish when she is not here," she said to Gratiano. "If she were present, there would be trouble at your home."

Not one drop of blood

"We are wasting time," said Shylock.

"Take your pound of flesh," said Portia. "The law allows it and the court gives it to you."

As Shylock began to move towards Antonio, Portia spoke again.

10

"Wait!" she said. "There is something else. Antonio has promised to give you a pound of his flesh. But he has not promised to give you any of his blood. If you let one drop of his blood fall, you will lose all your land and all your money."

"Oh, learned judge! Oh, wise young man!" cried Gratiano.

"Is that the law?" asked Shylock.

"You shall see the law," replied Portia. "You wanted judgement; so you shall get judgement – more than you wanted."

"I will take the money," said Shylock. "Give me three times more than Antonio borrowed from me."

"Here it is," Bassanio cried out, full of joy.

But Portia stopped him. "Wait!" she said. "Shylock would not take the money earlier. All he wanted was his pound of flesh. That is all he can have now: no more, no less, just one pound – and not one drop of blood."

Shylock turned to leave the court.

"Beg for mercy"

Portia had still not finished with Shylock.

"Wait, Shylock," she said. "The law of Venice says that if anyone tries to kill one of the people of Venice, everything that he owns shall be taken away from him. One half of his money and goods shall be given to the city of Venice and the other half shall be given to the person he has tried to kill. Your life is now at the mercy of the duke, so fall on your knees and beg for mercy."

"I shall not kill you," the great duke said. "But half of your money is now Antonio's. You must give the other half to the city of Venice."

"Take my life too!" cried Shylock. "My money and

11

Portia tells Shylock he cannot take any of Antonio's blood

goods are as dear to me as life itself. When you take those away from me, you take also my life."

"I shall be happy to give up my part of Shylock's money," said Antonio. "Shylock must promise to leave the money on his death to his daughter and her husband."

Shylock promised.

"Let me go home," he said. "I am not well."

Then the duke set Antonio free.

The rings

Antonio and Bassanio were left alone with Portia: they were full of thanks to her. They tried to give her money, but Portia would take nothing at all.

"Dear sir," said Bassanio. "Please take something so that you may remember us. We know that you do not want us to pay you, but we wish to give you something in order to show our thanks to you."

Portia pretended suddenly to notice a beautiful ring on Bassanio's finger. It was the ring that she had given to Bassanio in Belmont.

"Give me your ring," she said. "I shall wear it so that I can always remember you."

Bassanio had promised to wear the ring for ever.

"This ring," he said, "is too poor a present to give to you."

"I'll take nothing else," said Portia.

"I'll give you the best ring in Venice," said Bassanio. "But I can't give you this ring. My wife gave it to me. She made me promise never to sell it, nor to give it away, nor to lose it."

"If your wife knew what I have done for you, she wouldn't want you to keep the ring," said Portia, as she walked away angrily.

"Let the judge have the ring," said Antonio. "He should have much more than a ring after all he has done for us."

Bassanio thought again about the ring. He felt that he must show his deep thanks to the young judge and he knew that Antonio was right. At last he changed his mind and sent Gratiano after Portia with the ring.

When Gratiano brought the ring to Portia, he met Nerissa again. The two ladies were still dressed like men, so he did not know who they really were.

Nerissa had also given Gratiano a ring in Belmont. She said quietly to Portia, "I'll see if I can get my husband's ring that he too promised to keep for ever!"

Gratiano and Nerissa

Portia and Nerissa returned to Belmont, and Bassanio and Antonio came after them.

As soon as Bassanio arrived, he took Antonio to Portia and told her about everything that had happened. While the three of them were talking, Nerissa and Gratiano began to quarrel.

"A quarrel already?" asked Portia. "What's the matter?"

"It's only about a poor little ring that Nerissa gave me," replied Gratiano.

Gratiano tried to laugh about it, but Nerissa pretended to be very unhappy.

"You promised me that you would wear it until you died," cried Nerissa.

"I gave it to a young man," Gratiano said. "He was only a boy, no taller than you. He was the servant of the wise judge and he asked me for it."

Portia was enjoying this, but she did not laugh! She said solemnly, "It was wrong of you to give away your ring,

Gratiano. You promised to wear it for ever. I also gave my husband a ring. He would never give it away for all the money in the world."

The happy ending

Gratiano said, "Bassanio gave his ring away, too. He gave his ring to the wise young judge; and then the boy, the judge's servant, wanted mine."

Portia turned to Bassanio. "You have broken your promise to me!" she said. "I shall never love you until I see the ring again."

"I gave the ring to a judge who wouldn't take the three thousand ducats I offered him. He had just saved the life of my dearest friend. What else could I do?"

"I pray you to forgive him," said Antonio. "I once lent my body so that Bassanio could come to marry you. I should be dead now if the young judge hadn't saved me. I promise you, upon my life, that Bassanio will always be a good husband to you."

"Then," replied Portia, "give him this ring and tell him to keep it better than the other."

"It's the same ring that I gave to the wise young judge!" cried Bassanio.

"And I was that young judge," said Portia. "And here is my servant, that little boy! Nerissa was my servant!"

But that was not all. Portia gave Antonio a letter. The letter told Antonio that three of his ships had just returned safely to Venice.

"Come," said Portia. "It is almost morning, and I am sure that we all have many more questions to ask and answer. Let us go in and we will answer all things fully."

"Let it be so," said Gratiano. "Come, young servant of the wise judge – or would you rather be my wife?"

A Midsummer Night's Dream

"Marry Demetrius, or ..."

There was once in Greece a law which made young women very unhappy. This law said that a father could choose any man and make his daughter marry him.

One day an old man brought his beautiful daughter Hermia to the Duke of Athens. Athens was the biggest city in Greece, and the duke was a very powerful man. Everyone in Athens obeyed the duke.

"I have come to tell you about my daughter Hermia," said the old man. Then he turned and pointed to two young men who had come with Hermia. One of the young men was called Demetrius and the other was called Lysander. "I have ordered Hermia to marry Demetrius, but she won't do it. She loves Lysander, and she wants to marry him. Please tell her about the old law of Athens."

"Your father should be like a god to you," said the duke. "And you should do as your father wishes. Demetrius is a good man."

"So is Lysander; he is a good man too," said Hermia.

Then Lysander spoke to Hermia's father and the duke.

"I am as good and as rich as Demetrius," he said. "I love Hermia and she loves me. Why shouldn't I marry her? There is something else," he added. "Demetrius once loved Hermia's friend, Helena, and Helena loves Demetrius. Let him marry Helena."

The duke was very powerful and kind, but he could not change the laws of Athens.

"You must do what your father tells you to do," he said to Hermia. "Think carefully about this matter. In four days you must marry Demetrius."

Helena

When Lysander and Hermia were alone together later, Lysander said: "Listen to me, Hermia. Let's go away from Athens and get married. Leave your father's house tomorrow night and meet me in the wood outside Athens. I'll be waiting for you there."

"And I'll meet you there," said Hermia. "I promise you!"

"Keep that promise, dear Hermia!" said Lysander. "Look! Here comes Helena!"

"Ah! Beautiful Helena," cried Hermia. "Where are you going?"

"Don't call me beautiful. Demetrius loves you: he loves your eyes, your voice and everything about you. Oh, teach me how you look and how you speak, so that I can win his heart!"

"I don't want Demetrius to love me," said Hermia. "But the more I hate him, the more he follows me."

"The more I love him," said Helena, "the more he hates me!"

"Don't be sad," said Hermia. "He won't see my face again. Tomorrow Lysander and I are going to leave Athens. And then I hope you may have Demetrius."

When Helena was at last alone, she began to think about Hermia and Lysander: "Demetrius doesn't love me because he loves only Hermia. I'll go and tell him about their plan. Then he can follow Hermia. He doesn't love me, but he will at least thank me for telling him; and I shall be able to go there and come back with him."

Titania and Oberon

The next evening there were a great many people in the wood where Lysander had arranged to meet Hermia. But these people were not like other people: they were fairies. Oberon and Titania, the king and queen of the fairies, were holding their evening dances in the wood.

But only a short time before this, the fairy king and queen had quarrelled. Titania had a little boy who was her servant. Titania did not want to give the little boy to Oberon, so Oberon became very angry.

On that evening Titania was walking through the wood with all her fairy servants when she met Oberon.

"This is a bad meeting on such a beautiful night," said Oberon. "I am your master. Why do you quarrel with me? I only ask you to give me your little boy."

"Don't ask me for him any more!" said Titania. "All your fairy money won't buy this child from me. The boy's mother is dead. She was one of my favourite servants. Come, fairies! We shall get angry if we stay."

Titania and her fairy servants danced away under the bright light of the moon.

"Well! Go!" cried Oberon, "but before you leave this wood, I'll make you sad and sorry for what you have said."

Puck

Then Oberon called Puck, his chief servant. Puck was able to fly very quickly to any place. He loved to do things to people which would make them angry or cause other people to laugh at them. He went in front of people who were travelling by night and led them into strange places.

"Come here, Puck," called Oberon. "Bring me the flower that young girls call Love-in-Idleness. When the liquid from it is poured on the eyes of someone who is sleeping, it will make that man or woman fall in love with the next person he sees. Bring the flower to me as quickly as you can."

"I'll fly round the earth in forty minutes," said Puck, and he flew away.

"I'll find Titania when she's sleeping," said Oberon. "Then I'll drop some of the liquid from the flower on her eyes. When she opens her eyes, she'll fall in love with the first thing she sees, even if it's a bear, a wolf, a monkey, or any other beast. I'll make her give her little boy to me before I take this magic liquid away from her eyes."

Helena and Demetrius

While Puck was looking for the magic flower, Demetrius and Helena passed through the wood near Oberon. Demetrius was of course following Hermia and Lysander, but he did not want Helena to go with him.

"I can never love you, Helena," he said. "So don't follow me."

"But I love you," said Helena. "I only ask you to treat me like your dog and let me follow you."

Oberon was watching them. They could not see the fairy king, but he saw and heard everything they did. He felt sad when he heard Demetrius telling Helena that he did not love her. And he felt even sadder when he listened to Helena's gentle replies.

Soon Puck returned with the magic flower and Oberon took part of it to put on Titania's eyes. Then he remembered poor Helena and wanted to help her.

"Take some of this flower and go through the wood," he commanded Puck. "A sweet lady from Athens is in love with a young man who doesn't love her. Put some of the liquid from the magic flower on his eyes when he is sleeping, but be certain that the lady is near him. Meet me here before the morning comes."

So Puck flew away to carry out Oberon's orders.

The magic liquid

Oberon said, "I know a bank that is covered with sweet-smelling flowers. That is where Titania sleeps."

He found Titania giving orders to her fairy servants before she went to bed. Then she said, "First sing me to sleep, and then go and do your work."

As soon as Titania fell asleep, the fairies left to do the things that their queen had ordered. Then Oberon came and poured the magic liquid on her eyes.

"You will fall in love with the first thing you see when you awaken," he cried. "Open your eyes when something ugly is near."

Bottom and the donkey's head

While Oberon was pouring the magic liquid over Titania's eyes, Puck was looking everywhere for Demetrius. On his way through the big wood, Puck saw some workmen from Athens. These workmen were simple people and were preparing to act in a play. They were going to give the play at the marriage of the Duke of Athens.

Puck thought that these players were very foolish. The most foolish of them was called Bottom. When Bottom left the others, Puck followed him and changed his head into a donkey's head.

Bottom did not know that his head had been changed. He came back to his friends when it was time for him to speak in the play. When the other workmen saw Bottom with a donkey's head, they ran away.

"Why have they run away?" Bottom wondered.

Oberon with the magic flower

"They're trying to make me afraid. But I'm not afraid! I'll sing, and then they'll hear that I'm not afraid."

So he began to sing loudly – with his donkey's voice.

Titania was sleeping not far away. She suddenly woke up when she heard the loud noise. She opened her eyes and of course the first person she saw was Bottom. The liquid from the magic flower began to work, and she fell in love with the big, ugly Bottom.

"What beautiful fairy awakens me from my sleep?" she said. "Please sing again. I love to hear your voice and see you. You must stay here. I love you. Come with me and I shall give you fairies to serve you. They will give you jewels and sing for you."

Bottom among the fairies

Titania called for four of her fairy servants.

"Be kind to this sweet gentleman," she said. "Dance round him when he walks. Play in his sight. Feed him with fruit, and steal food from the bees for him."

Although Titania was deeply in love with the foolish Bottom, even she soon grew tired of hearing him talk.

"Bring him to my fairy garden and tie up his tongue," she ordered.

When they reached this beautiful part of the wood, Titania spoke again to Bottom.

"Come, sit with me upon this bed of flowers," she said. "Let me gently touch the hair on your face. Then I'll put roses on your head and kiss your beautiful big ears."

Bottom felt very proud of himself and he loved to have fairy servants.

"Rub my head, Peas-blossom," ordered Bottom.

Then Bottom asked for another fairy, called Cobweb.

"I want some honey – the sweet liquid of the bees.

Where's Mustard-seed?"

"Ready," said Mustard-seed. "What do you want?"

"Nothing," answered Bottom. Then he thought again. "Help Peas-blossom to rub my head. I must ask someone to cut my hair. I think my face is very hairy."

"What do you want to eat, my sweet love?" Titania asked.

"I want some dried grass," answered Bottom. "But don't let anyone wake me. I think I'll go to sleep."

"Sleep in my arms, then," said Titania. "I love you so much!"

Hermia and Lysander

After Puck had given Bottom the donkey's head, he went to look for Demetrius. At last, he saw a young man from Athens asleep in the wood. A beautiful lady was asleep not far away.

Puck made certain that the beautiful lady was quite near the young man. Then he poured some of the magic liquid on the eyes of the man.

"Now he'll see her when he wakes, and he'll fall in love with her." Puck laughed as he flew off to tell Oberon what he had done.

But Puck did not know that the young man he had seen was Lysander, and not Demetrius. The beautiful lady sleeping not far away was Hermia, of course. Things would have been all right if Lysander had woken and seen Hermia. But that did not happen.

Helena had grown tired of running after Demetrius. She could not follow him any further and she wandered sadly through the wood. Soon she arrived at the place where Lysander was sleeping.

When she saw Lysander, Helena wondered whether he

Bottom and Titania

was dead or asleep. She did not see any blood or a wound, so she woke him.

Lysander opened his eyes; the magic liquid did its work, and he fell in love with Helena – the first person he saw.

"Oh, Helena!" he cried. "You are so beautiful! I would run through fire for you. I wish I had never loved Hermia, for now I love nobody but you. You're much more beautiful than Hermia. Demetrius has been cruel to you: I shall kill Demetrius."

"Don't say these things," said Helena. "Demetrius loves your Hermia; but she loves you and you love her."

"No! I don't. I don't love Hermia. I love you, Helena."

"Why are you so unkind to me? Why are you making fun of me?"

She went sadly away into the wood again. But Lysander was not pretending; he really was in love with Helena now. So he left Hermia alone in the wood and ran after Helena.

Soon after Lysander had left her, Hermia woke up. She cried out with fear because she had had a bad dream. She called out to Lysander, but he was not near her. She was alone and afraid.

Hermia and Demetrius

Hermia went to look for Lysander, whom she had always loved; but she met Demetrius.

"Where is Lysander?" she cried angrily.

"Why are you angry with me, when I love you so much?"

"I'm angry," said Hermia, "because I believe that you have killed Lysander. If you have killed him, kill me, too! Or tell me where he is."

"I don't know where he is."

Hermia ran away.

"It's useless to follow her when she's like this!" said Demetrius. "I'll stay here and get some sleep."

Oberon and Puck had been watching Demetrius and Hermia, and they had heard every word they said.

"What have you done?" said Oberon to Puck. "You have put the liquid on the eyes of the wrong man! I'll put it in this man's eyes. He must wake and love Helena. Go! Go quickly and bring Helena here before he wakes."

The mixed-up lovers

So Puck led Helena to the place where Demetrius was sleeping. She was followed by Lysander, who was still talking about his love for her.

"Why are you making fun of me?" said Helena.

"I love you!"

"Tell that to Hermia!"

The sound of their voices woke Demetrius. Helena was the first woman he saw, so he fell in love with her.

"Oh, Helena!" he cried. "Beautiful Helena! Your eyes are like jewels. Oh, let me kiss you, my princess!"

"I see that you both want to make fun of me! Hate me, as I know you do, but don't join together to hurt me."

"You are unkind, Demetrius," said Lysander. "You love Hermia; I know you do. I give you Hermia, but let me love Helena. I love her and will love her till I die."

"Lysander, keep your Hermia!" cried Demetrius. "All my love for her has gone."

So both Lysander and Demetrius shouted that they loved Helena.

Then Hermia came, and saw Lysander.

"Why did you leave me alone in the wood?" she asked.

"I left you because I love Helena now."

Hermia did not believe him. Helena now thought that all three had made a plan to hurt her.

"Why have you joined in this plan to make a fool of me?" she asked Hermia angrily. "You are very unkind to laugh at me. I'll go back to Athens and not follow you any more. I leave my foolish heart behind."

Lysander cried, "Helena, I love you!"

"I love you more than he does," shouted Demetrius.

The two men were growing angrier and angrier. They walked away to another part of the wood to fight each other for Helena's love.

Oberon gives orders

"Demetrius and Lysander have gone to look for a good place to fight," said Oberon to Puck. "Fill the night with a thick, black cloud. Then lead the two men far from each other. When they are tired of looking for each other, they'll lie down and fall asleep. Pour this magic liquid on Lysander's eyes. It will make his old love for Hermia come back to him when he wakes. Then everyone will be happy. They'll think that all this has been only a dream. While you do that, I'll go to Titania. I'll take the little boy from her. Then I'll set her free and she will stop loving the foolish man with the donkey's head."

Music!

When Oberon found Titania, she was asleep. She had put beautiful flowers round Bottom's donkey's head. Oberon found it easy to take the little boy from her while she was sleeping. Then he was ready to take away the magic liquid from her eyes. He touched her eyes with another flower and gently woke her.

"My Oberon!" Titania cried. "What dreams I have had! I thought I was in love with a donkey."

"There he is," replied Oberon, pointing to Bottom, asleep near Titania.

"How did this happen?" asked Titania. "I can't bear the sight of him now."

Puck came back after doing as Oberon had ordered. Oberon turned to him and said:

"Take off the donkey's head, and make all these five – Bottom, Demetrius, Lysander, Helena, and Hermia – fall into a deep sleep and forget what has happened."

"Music!" cried Titania.

"Music!" cried Oberon. "Come, my queen, take hands with me and dance – dance round the world faster than the wandering moon."

To Athens

Early that morning, the Duke of Athens and Hermia's father entered the forest. They came with a great many friends and servants. They reached the place where Hermia, Helena, Lysander, and Demetrius were sleeping. The four young people were woken by the voices of the duke and his friends.

Lysander now loved only Hermia, and Demetrius loved only Helena.

The wise duke knew that this was a good ending. He did not want to make Hermia marry Demetrius now. And Hermia's father knew that he could never order the marriage between his daughter and Demetrius.

"Lysander shall marry Hermia," said the duke, "and Demetrius shall marry Helena. Come with us to Athens, where I, too, am to be married. Let's go to Athens at once. There we'll all be married."

Hamlet

Hamlet's sorrow

Gertrude was the Queen of Denmark. Two months after the death of the King of Denmark, she married Claudius, his brother. She did not know that Claudius was evil. People believed that he had killed his brother so that he himself might become king – instead of Hamlet. Hamlet was the son of Gertrude and the king who had just died.

Hamlet loved his dead father and was very sad at his death. His mother's marriage made Hamlet even more unhappy. He became tired of the world; he had no more pleasure in the things he used to do. He stopped wanting to read, to play, and to do all the things that young men love to do. "Why has my mother so soon forgotten my father?" he thought. "He was such a good husband to her, and so good a father to me."

Claudius said to Hamlet: "Now, Hamlet, you are like a son to me. Why are you so unhappy?"

"Try not to think so much about your dead father," said Hamlet's mother. "You know that everything that lives must die some time. Why do you still seem to be sad?"

"I am not just pretending to be sad," said Hamlet. "I wear my black clothes because I really am sad at my father's death."

Neither Hamlet's mother nor Claudius could do anything to make Hamlet happier. He would not take off his black clothes and he would not laugh. He felt angry that his mother should marry a man as evil as his uncle.

Horatio speaks

Horatio, Hamlet's friend, came to him and told him a strange story. Horatio said, "The spirit of your father was seen on the walls of the castle in the middle of the night. It has visited the castle on two or three nights and the guards have been very frightened. I saw it: it was dressed like the old king before a battle. I tried to speak to it, but it didn't answer."

"Did you see its face?" said Hamlet.

"Yes, we did," Horatio answered. "It seemed sad rather than angry."

"I shall watch tonight," said Hamlet. "Perhaps it will come again. I'll speak to it. I'll come to you on the walls between eleven and twelve. Say nothing about this."

Horatio went away.

"My father's ghost!" Hamlet thought. "Something is wrong. Evil can't be hidden. When night comes, I shall know."

The ghost

When night came, Hamlet joined the soldiers who were guarding the walls. Suddenly Horatio cried out. The ghost had appeared again!

When he saw his father's ghost, Hamlet soon forgot his fear and spoke bravely to it.

"Whether you are something good or something bad, I'll speak to you. You appear to be so much like my father that I shall call you by your name – Hamlet, King, Father! Tell me why you have come and what we should do to help you."

The ghost held up its hand and pointed away from the soldiers.

"It wants to speak to you alone," cried Horatio. "Don't

go with it; it may lead you into the sea or take you to the top of a high cliff."

Hamlet was not afraid. He followed the ghost.

As soon as Hamlet and the ghost were alone, the ghost spoke. "I am the ghost of your father. I must walk in the night until the wrongs done while I was alive are set right. Listen! Claudius killed your father. When he was sleeping he poured poisonous liquid into his ears and caused his death. He killed his brother, and then he took his crown and his queen. And this man, Claudius, is now King of Denmark! Evil must be paid for! He must die. Deal with him. But do not hurt your mother."

"I promise. I'll forget everything I have learned from books," said Hamlet. "I shall remember only my promise to you!"

When Hamlet's friends ran up to him, they asked him to tell them what the ghost had said. But Hamlet did not tell even his best friend what had happened.

"Promise me that you will never tell anyone what you have seen tonight," he said. "And, if I seem to act strangely, don't tell anyone the cause."

Hamlet did not want Claudius to think that anything was wrong. So he pretended to be mad. He even pretended to Ophelia, the beautiful lady whom he loved, that he was mad.

The actors

Claudius, who trusted no one, sent for two young men who had been Hamlet's friends when they were all children. Claudius wanted them to try to find out the reason for Hamlet's strange ways.

When Hamlet saw them, he wondered why they had come to visit him.

Hamlet makes a promise to his father's ghost

"Why did you come here?" he asked. "Were you ordered to come, or did you come freely?"

"We were sent for."

"I'll tell you why you were sent for," said Hamlet. "I have lately lost all my joy in the beauty of the earth and sky. Man is a wonderful thing – so wise, so beautiful; but man does not please me now, nor woman."

"Perhaps these players may please you. They are coming to act a play in the castle."

Soon the actors arrived, and Hamlet was very pleased to see them. He asked one of the actors to say a few lines to him, telling about the death of an old king. The actor told how the old king was killed and his city was burned. Then he spoke about the sad queen, who ran about the castle with a cloth on her head instead of a crown. The actor told the story so well that he even had tears in his eyes.

When Hamlet saw the actor weeping, he felt very angry with himself.

"This actor can weep for a queen he never knew," thought Hamlet. "But I have done nothing at all about my father's death."

Suddenly he thought of a plan. "I'll ask the actors to act a story which is like the death of my father. I'll ask Claudius to see the play and see what he himself did. This may prove to me that Claudius killed my father. Then I shall be completely certain that the ghost spoke the truth."

The play

That evening Hamlet met Horatio. He said to his old friend, "Watch Claudius carefully during the play. Watch his face."

When the actors were ready to begin the play, Hamlet sat next to Ophelia. Claudius, who knew nothing of

Hamlet's plan, was there with the queen and all their friends.

The play began. The queen in the play told the king how much she loved him. She promised never to marry a second husband if the king died before her.

"Only women who kill their husbands marry again," she said.

The king in the play fell asleep in his garden and was killed by his brother's son.

Claudius stood up. He could bear no more of the play. It was so much like the way in which he had killed his own brother.

"What is it, my lord?" asked the queen. "What is the matter?"

Polonius cried, "Stop the play!"

"Light! Light!" shouted the king. "Away! All go away!"

Hamlet was sure now that the ghost had spoken the truth. He was now certain that his uncle had killed his father. All that remained for him to do was to carry out the ghost's command.

Hamlet's mother

The queen sent a servant to Hamlet asking him to go to her room. While he was on his way to his mother's room, he saw Claudius kneeling and praying. It seemed to him that Claudius was telling God about the evil that he had done.

"I can kill him now," thought Hamlet, "but if I kill him while he is praying, he'll go to heaven. I must choose another time to kill him – when he is angry or asleep."

Ophelia's father, Polonius, was hiding behind a curtain in the queen's room. He had promised Claudius that he would hide and listen to everything Hamlet said. The queen knew that Polonius was there.

Hamlet went into the queen's room.

"What's the matter, mother?" he asked.

"You have made your father very angry."

"My father! Claudius is not my father. You have done a great wrong to my father."

"Have you forgotten who I am?" said the queen.

"No! You are the queen, wife of your husband's brother, and you are my mother. I wish you were not! No, do not move. Sit down, while I tell you all about yourself."

"What! Do you want to kill me?" she cried. Then she shouted, "Help! Help!"

The death of Polonius

When he heard the queen's cry, Polonius shouted from behind the curtain, "Help! Help!"

"What is it? A rat?" cried Hamlet. He drew his sword and struck through the curtain. He thought that Claudius was hiding there, and he hoped that he had killed him. Then he drew back the curtain and saw that he had killed Polonius.

"Oh! What have you done?" cried the queen.

"What I have done," said Hamlet, "is almost as bad a thing as killing a king and marrying his brother."

"How dare you speak to me like that?"

"How could you forget about my father so quickly and be happy with my uncle? What made you marry him? You can't call it love, because at your age the blood is cold. What was it that made you blind?"

"Oh, Hamlet, say no more!" the queen cried.

"How can you live with such a man – a man not worth the twentieth part of your first husband?"

"Say no more! No more!"

The ghost again

As Hamlet became more and more angry, the ghost appeared before him.

"Oh!" Hamlet cried. "Have you come to tell me that, in my anger, I have forgotten to do what I have promised?"

"He's mad," the queen said to herself.

"Do not forget your promise," said the ghost. "But see how afraid your mother is. Speak to her, Hamlet. Help her."

"What's the matter, mother?" said Hamlet.

"What's the matter with *you*?" cried the queen. "You look at nothing, and speak to it. Oh, my son, what are you looking at?"

"At him! At him!"

"Who are you speaking to?"

"Can't you see anything there? Can't you hear anything?" cried Hamlet.

"Nothing at all."

"Look there! See how he moves away. It's my father."

"There is no ghost. You see it because you are mad," his mother replied.

"I am not mad. My father's ghost has come here because of what you have done. Pray to God to forgive you. Don't go back to the king and don't behave as his wife any more."

"You *are* mad!"

"I'm not mad; but you may let Claudius think I'm mad, and don't tell him what I have said to you. Promise me that. Good night."

To England

Claudius knew that something was wrong when he saw Hamlet's mother.

"How is Hamlet?" he asked.

"He's as mad as the sea and the wind when they fight each other," cried the queen. "When he heard something move behind the curtain in my room, he cried in his mad anger, 'A rat! A rat!' and killed Polonius."

Claudius said, "The mad young prince is dangerous. We must send him away to England."

He sent for Hamlet and said, "I am sending you to England so that you may be safe. The people of Denmark may try to kill you when they hear how Polonius died. Get ready quickly; the ship is waiting."

Claudius did not tell Hamlet that he had written a letter to the King of England. He sent this letter with Hamlet's two "friends", and they knew that in it he asked the king to kill Hamlet as soon as he reached England.

Hamlet's escape

When he was at sea, Hamlet began to feel certain that Claudius had planned some evil. He did not trust his two "friends". One night he got up and looked for the letter that his friends were carrying. He opened the letter and read that Claudius had asked the King of England to kill him. He changed the names in the letter so that it asked the King of England to kill his two "friends".

The next day, Hamlet's ship met some pirates, who attacked the ship to take its goods. During the battle Hamlet jumped on the pirates' ship to fight. While he was there, his own ship sailed away.

The pirates were kind to Hamlet when they found out that he was a prince. They made him promise to do something for them later in return for his freedom. They put him safely on shore in Denmark.

Ophelia's grave

When Hamlet returned home the next day, he saw two old men digging a grave.

"Whose grave is this?" he asked.

But the old men did not say that it was Ophelia's grave.

Ophelia had begun to grow mad when Hamlet killed Polonius, her father. She could hardly believe that the man she loved had done such a thing. She began to gather flowers and give them to the people at the court. One day she wanted to get some flowers from the branch of a tree over a stream. While she was climbing on the branch, it suddenly broke, and Ophelia fell. Her dress, heavy with water, pulled her down to the bottom, and she died.

While Hamlet was at the grave, the king and queen and their servants came, carrying the body of Ophelia. Laertes, her brother, was with them.

Hamlet saw Laertes standing near the grave and talking about Ophelia.

Then he saw the queen throw some flowers on the grave.

"Sweet flowers to a sweet lady," said the queen. "I hoped that you would be my Hamlet's wife. I wanted to throw flowers on your marriage-bed, not on your grave."

Suddenly Laertes cried, "Don't throw any more earth into the grave. Let me hold her once more in my arms!" Then he jumped wildly into Ophelia's grave.

Hamlet ran forward and jumped into the grave beside Laertes.

"I loved Ophelia more than forty thousand brothers could love her," he shouted.

At once Laertes began to fight Hamlet. The servants who were standing near the grave stopped the two angry men. They pulled them out of the grave. Hamlet could not understand why Laertes was so angry with him. He did not know that Claudius wanted Laertes to kill Hamlet, and so he had told Laertes lies about the way Polonius, his father, was killed.

Hamlet's death is planned

After Hamlet had left Ophelia's grave, Claudius spoke again to Laertes about their plan to kill Hamlet.

They planned to arrange a duel with swords between Laertes and Hamlet. The swords that were used in such duels were not dangerous: they had something on the end which covered their points. Claudius told Laertes to use a sword without anything on the end. This sword would be very dangerous and could kill a man.

Laertes wanted to make certain that he would kill Hamlet, so they also planned to put some poison on the point of his sword. Claudius promised to give Hamlet some poison to drink if Laertes did not wound him.

The duel

Laertes entered the big hall of the castle with the king and queen and their servants.

Hamlet tried to act like a friend. "Come," he said, "let us have a friendly fight."

At first Hamlet seemed to be winning. Claudius offered him the cup of poison, but Hamlet did not drink it. "I'll drink it later," he said. But the queen wanted to show Hamlet how happy she was to see him winning. So she picked up the cup of poison and drank it.

Soon Laertes wounded Hamlet with his poisoned sword. In the fight which followed, Hamlet and Laertes dropped their swords and, by mistake, Hamlet picked up

Hamlet fights with Laertes

Laertes' sword. Then he wounded Laertes with the poisoned sword.

Suddenly the queen fell to the floor.

"The queen!" Hamlet cried. "What's the matter?"

"She feels sick at the sight of the blood running from your wound," said Claudius.

But before she died, the queen cried, "The drink, the drink. It's poison!"

Hamlet dies

"Shut all the doors!" cried Hamlet.

Laertes fell, wounded and poisoned.

"Nothing can save you, Hamlet," he cried. "I have wounded you with a poisoned sword. I have been wounded with it too. Your mother has drunk a cup of poison. The king has caused all this to happen."

Hamlet looked at the sword in his hand. "Poisoned and sharp!" he said. He ran towards Claudius. "Here is the best place for a poisoned sword," he cried, as he drove the point into the king's heart.

Then he watched Claudius fall and die.

"It is right that the king should die," cried the dying Laertes. "He mixed the poison which has killed him. Forgive me, Hamlet. It was not you who caused my father's death and mine."

Hamlet knew that he was dying. He turned to his oldest friend, Horatio. "Horatio," he said. "I am dying. Tell the world what has happened."

"There is still some poison left in this cup," cried Horatio. "I shall die, too."

"Don't drink it, if you ever loved me," Hamlet cried. "You must live and tell my story to the world. Then people will know the truth. – The rest is silence."

Julius Caesar

"I am Caesar"

About two thousand years ago a great man named Julius Caesar lived in Rome. He ruled Rome wisely, but he began to grow very proud. He had great power, but he wanted even more. Many people thought he wanted to become a king, although the people of Rome offered him a crown three times, and each time he said "No".

There were a few men who thought that Julius Caesar had too much power.

"We are all free men, Brutus," said Cassius, an important Roman. "I am as free as Caesar. He should not be a king or a god: he is only a man like me. Why do the people of Rome let him act like a god?"

Brutus was a friend of Caesar's, but he was also troubled by what was happening to Caesar. "I am afraid that the people want Caesar for their king," he said. "I love Caesar, but I don't want him to become king."

Mark Antony was Caesar's closest friend. Caesar trusted him more than any other man. Caesar saw Cassius talking to Brutus. "Let me have men around me who are fat," said Caesar. "Cassius is thin and has a hungry look. He thinks too much. Such men are dangerous."

"Don't be afraid of him," said Antony. "He isn't dangerous."

"I wish he were fatter. I am not afraid, but I keep away from him. He reads a lot; he watches men. He never laughs. Such men as he are never happy when they can see a man who is greater than themselves."

"Don't be afraid," said Mark Antony. "Cassius isn't dangerous. He's a good Roman."

"I'm not afraid of him," Caesar replied proudly. "I'm not afraid of anyone, because I am Caesar."

Brutus decides

That night there was a great storm. Many strange things happened. It was the biggest storm that men had ever seen. Wild animals ran through the streets of the city, but did not hurt anyone. Men covered in fire walked about Rome. The old men in the city knew that something bad was going to happen.

Brutus was still very unhappy about Caesar. After his talk with Cassius, he could not trust Caesar.

"Caesar must die," Brutus decided. "He isn't my enemy as a man, but for the good of all he ought to die. He wants to be king: that will change him and will make him dangerous."

A servant came and said, "I found this letter near the window. It wasn't there when I went to bed."

Brutus read the letter: "Brutus, you are asleep. Awake and see yourself. Shall Rome be under one man's rule? Speak! Strike!"

The plan

Just as Brutus finished reading this letter, his servant came to tell him that Cassius and some other men had come to see him. Their faces were hidden. Brutus knew that they had come to plan Caesar's death.

Cassius and his friends were not sure that Brutus wanted to join them in their plan to kill Caesar. Then Cassius took Brutus to one side and spoke softly to him.

Brutus turned to the others and shook hands with each one of them to show that he would join in their plan.

"Let us make a solemn promise to kill Caesar," said Cassius.

"We have already promised to do it," Brutus replied. "We are good Romans. No true Roman needs to make a solemn promise to keep him to his duty."

"We ought to kill Caesar's friend, Mark Antony, too," said Cassius. "He may become dangerous if we kill Caesar. It is safer if he and Caesar die together."

"No," said Brutus. "We must not do more killing than we need. If we kill Antony, that would be like cutting off a man's head and then cutting off his arms. Antony is only like an arm of Caesar's."

"But I'm afraid of him," said Cassius.

"I wish that we could kill Caesar's spirit and not his body," said Brutus. 'We aren't going to kill Caesar because we don't like him. Let everyone see that we are killing Caesar only because it is necessary for the good of Rome."

Brutus and his friends then arranged to meet Caesar the following day and kill him on his way to the Senate.

Calpurnia

Caesar's wife was troubled and afraid that night.

Caesar said, "There is no peace in heaven or earth tonight. Three times my wife, Calpurnia, cried out in her sleep: 'Help! Help! They are killing Caesar.' "

Calpurnia came to him. "Don't leave your home today," she said. "You have enemies. Many things tell of danger to you."

"I shall go," said Caesar. "When my enemies see my face, they will be afraid. Men who fear death die many times; but brave men die only once. It seems strange to me that men should be afraid to die. Death is a necessary end and it will come when it will come."

A servant entered. "The wise men," he said, "say that you should not leave the house today. They have killed an animal and cut open its body. They looked for anything which seemed strange and found that the animal had no heart. Therefore they say that you must not go."

"I should be like an animal without a heart if I stayed at home," said Caesar.

"Oh, my lord," cried Calpurnia. "You are brave – too brave – but you are not wise. Don't go out today. Say that it is my fear, not yours, which keeps you in the house. We'll send Mark Antony and he can say that you are not well today."

"Well," said Caesar, "to please you I will stay at home. Mark Antony shall say that I am not well."

Decius speaks

Caesar had just decided this when Decius, Cassius's friend, arrived. Decius had come to take Caesar to meet all the other people who ruled Rome, the Senate. He had promised Cassius and Brutus to make certain that Caesar left his house.

"Tell the people of Rome that I will not come out today," Caesar said. "My wife has asked me to stay at home: she had bad dreams about me, and is afraid for my life!"

"The people are going to give you a crown today," said Decius. "If you don't come, they may change their minds. And everyone will laugh at you. They'll say that you can't come until your wife has better dreams. If Caesar doesn't come, they'll say 'Caesar is afraid.' "

Caesar said, "How foolish your fears seem now, Calpurnia! I should not have listened to them ... I will go."

Then Caesar left the house to go to his death.

"Strike!"

Caesar entered the Senate House.

"Look, Brutus," said Casca. "Our friend Trebonius is leading Mark Antony away. Where's Metellus? He must go and speak to Caesar about his brother whom Caesar sent away from Rome."

"Metellus is there," said Brutus. "Come, let's press round them. Casca, you must strike first."

Metellus fell on his knees before Caesar. "Most high, most powerful Caesar, I pray you——"

"Get up!" said Caesar. "If you kneel before me like that, I shall treat you as a dog."

"I pray you, Caesar, allow my brother to return to Rome ... Will no one speak for me?"

"I kiss your hand, Caesar," said Brutus, "and pray that he may be allowed to return."

"Prayers may move other men," answered Caesar. "They change, but I do not change. I am fixed, like a star. There is no other star like me in the sky. I ordered him to go. My order will not be changed."

They pressed round him, crying, "Oh, Caesar! Great Caesar!" Then Casca cried out, "Strike!" and they struck Caesar with their swords. Brutus struck last.

"You too, Brutus?" cried Caesar as he fell.

Then Brutus cried out, "People and Senators, don't be afraid. We don't mean to hurt anyone. Come, let's put our hands in Caesar's blood and, holding our red swords above our heads, cry 'Peace and Freedom!' We shall be called the men who set Rome free."

Caesar in the Senate

Mark Antony

Antony had been with Caesar when he entered the building. As soon as Caesar was killed, Antony had gone home. Now his servant went to see Brutus. He asked if Antony might come safely to Brutus and learn the reason for Caesar's death.

Brutus said, "Your master is a wise and brave Roman. Ask him to come to this place. We shall tell him, and he will return safe."

When Antony arrived he stopped by Caesar's body and sadly said, "Oh, powerful Caesar, have all the great things that you have done ended in this?" Then he turned to Brutus and his friends. "I don't know, gentlemen, what your plans are. Who else must be killed? If it is me, kill me now – at the same time as the great Caesar and with the swords which are still red with his blood."

"Oh, Antony," cried Brutus. "Our swords are not meant for you. Our hands are bloody, but our hearts are sad: we have killed Caesar only for the good of Rome. We love you like a brother. Wait till we have spoken to the people. Then you shall know why I, who loved Caesar when I struck him, have done this."

"My friends," said Antony, "I do not doubt that you are wise. I am with you all and love you all. I hope that you will give me reasons, why Caesar was dangerous. Only I ask this. Let me take his body to the public square, where, as his friend, I may speak good of him."

Casca did not like this, but Brutus said, "I shall speak first and tell the reason for Caesar's death, and say that we have allowed Antony to speak in Caesar's honour."

"I don't know what will happen. I don't like it," said Casca. But Brutus and his friends left Antony alone with the body of Caesar.

Octavius

Antony looked sadly at the dead body of his friend; then he began to talk to Caesar as if he were alive.

"Oh, forgive me, Caesar, for being so gentle to the men who killed you. You were the greatest man who ever lived. I shall deal with those who killed you. There will be a long war, many will be killed and many things will be destroyed. I make this solemn promise to you: I shall not rest until Brutus and Cassius are dead."

Just then a servant arrived from Octavius Caesar. Octavius was the son of Julius Caesar's brother. Julius Caesar had sent for Octavius to come to Rome, and Octavius was now only a few miles outside the city. He did not know about his uncle's death that morning.

Antony said to the servant, "Go back and tell him what has happened. Rome isn't safe for him. No! Wait till I have spoken to the people, then you may tell Octavius how things are."

Brutus speaks to the people

The next day in the public square, Brutus told the people of Rome the reasons for Caesar's death. A large crowd had gathered to listen to him. He said:

"I loved Caesar as much as any of his friends. I killed Caesar because I loved Rome more. He wanted power. Did you want Caesar to live and make you all servants to him? Or do you want Caesar dead and to be free men? I shall kill myself with the same sword when it is for the good of Rome."

When Brutus had almost finished speaking to the crowd, Mark Antony and his servants carried Caesar's body into the public square.

The people cried, "Long live Brutus! Let him be Caesar!

Let him be ruler in Caesar's place! Let us carry him to his home!"

Brutus said, "Good people, let me leave alone. Stay here with Antony and listen to him. We have allowed him to speak in Caesar's honour."

"Let him speak," said one man, "but he mustn't speak against Brutus."

"It's a good thing that Caesar is dead," said another.

"Silence!" said the first man. "Let's hear what Antony has to say."

"Let's hear him," shouted all the people.

"Friends, Romans, countrymen"

Mark Antony began to speak.

"Friends, Romans, countrymen – men of my own country. The bad things that men do live after them; the good is often forgotten after their death. Caesar was my friend, true and just to me. When the poor cried, he wept. Brutus says that Caesar wanted more and more power. But I offered Caesar the crown three times, and he wouldn't take it. You all loved Caesar once: you had good reason to love him. Why do you not weep for him now?"

The men in the crowd began to talk.

"They have done wrong to Caesar," one man said.

"There isn't a nobler man in Rome than Antony. See how his eyes are red with weeping," another cried.

"Yesterday," said Antony, "Caesar was the most powerful man in the world; now he lies there. Look at him. I could move your hearts to anger against Brutus and Cassius, but that would be wrong, because, as you know, they are men whom we should honour. I would rather do wrong to the dead and to myself than to them."

Antony went on: "I have here a paper, written by

Mark Antony speaks to the people of Rome

Caesar. It is his will. It tells what is to be done with his money and land after his death. I won't read it. – If I read it to you, you would want to kiss Caesar's wounds."

"Read it! Read it!" cried the people.

"No. It isn't right that you should know how much Caesar loved you. It would make you angry."

"Read it! Read the will!" cried the people.

"I shouldn't read it. I am afraid that I may do wrong to the honourable men who killed Caesar."

"They aren't honourable men!" cried the people. "Read the will!"

"Stand in a ring round his body. Be ready to weep now. This is the place where Cassius's sword went through. Here is the hole that Casca made. Here was Brutus's sword; see how the blood followed it. Brutus was Caesar's truest friend. Caesar loved him. When he saw Brutus strike, great Caesar fell. Oh, what a fall was there! Then I and you and all of us fell down, while these men of blood stood over us. Ah! Now you weep."

"Oh, noble Caesar!" cried the people. "Oh, most bloody sight! Kill them! Burn their houses!"

"Why?" said Antony. "Why are you going to do these things? What has Caesar done to make you love him? You have forgotten the will – here it is. He gives each Roman seventy-five pieces of money. He leaves you all his gardens and his fields to walk and play in."

"We shall take his body to the Burning Place, and with the fire set fire to those men's houses," the crowd cried out.

Then they carried away Caesar's body.

"Now I have started something," said Antony. "Let's see what happens."

A servant came to him. "Octavius has come to Rome. Brutus and Cassius have gone out of the city."

Caesar's ghost

Brutus and Cassius saw too late how dangerous Antony was. They gathered an army and prepared to fight Antony and Octavius's men. Then Brutus and Cassius heard that Octavius and Antony were travelling towards Philippi, a place quite near their own army.

"Let us march to Philippi at once," said Brutus.

"No," said Cassius, "I don't think that will be wise. It is better for the enemy to look for us. Then their soldiers will be tired when we fight against them."

"The people between here and Philippi are our enemies," answered Brutus. "Antony's army will be able to gather more men as they come. Our own army is as strong as it will ever be. We must not miss this chance or it will be lost for ever."

Cassius was silent. He agreed to go with Brutus to Philippi to meet the enemy.

Brutus remained awake after Cassius had left his tent. Suddenly, the ghost of Caesar was standing before him.

"Why have you come?" cried Brutus.

"To tell you that you will see me at Philippi."

Philippi

Antony, Octavius, and their army were at Philippi.

"Now, Antony," said Octavius, "it is as we hoped. You feared that the enemy would stay up in the hills, but they have come down."

"I understand them," answered Antony. "They think that this will show us that they are not afraid."

Cassius was preparing for the battle, but he was not happy. He had seen great birds following his army, as if they were looking for dead men to feed on.

53

"If we lose this battle," said Cassius to Brutus, "you will be led a prisoner through the streets of Rome."

"No, Cassius," said Brutus, "don't think that! This day must end the work that we began when we killed Caesar. I don't know whether we shall meet again. So let's say goodbye. If we do meet again, we shall laugh at this. If we don't, it's good to say goodbye now."

The noblest Roman

Soon the battle began. At one time it seemed that Antony's army was winning and at another time it seemed that Brutus was winning. At last, Cassius's men began to fall back. Antony's soldiers set fire to the tents of Cassius's army. Cassius saw that his army was losing the battle. He did not want to be caught by Antony's men, so he asked one of his soldiers to kill him.

Brutus found Cassius dead at the foot of a hill. He looked at Cassius's own sword which was through the heart of his brave friend. He remembered Caesar's ghost and knew that he would lose the battle.

The fight continued, and one after another of Brutus's friends were killed. Brutus, with a few friends, heard the enemy coming nearer and nearer. But, like Cassius, Brutus was very brave and would not run away. He ordered a soldier to hold out his sword. Then Brutus threw himself upon it.

"Caesar, now be happy," he cried as he died. "I did not kill you half so willingly as I have killed myself."

Mark Antony looked down at the body of Brutus. "This was the noblest Roman of them all," he said. "All those others wanted Caesar's power. Brutus thought of nothing but the good of all the people. He was truly a great man."

Questions

Questions on each story

The Merchant of Venice
1 Who was Bassanio in love with?
2 Who hated Antonio?
3 What did Antonio agree to give Shylock if he couldn't pay?
4 Which box did the prince from Africa choose?
5 Which box did the French prince choose?
6 What gift from Portia did Bassanio promise to keep?
7 Why couldn't Antonio pay Shylock? (Because . . .)
8 What clothes did Portia borrow?
9 Who went into the court with Portia?
10 When did Shylock call Portia "wise"?
11 What must Shylock *not* take from Antonio?
12 What did Shylock promise to do with the money Antonio didn't take?
13 What did Portia take from Bassanio?
14 What did Nerissa take from Gratiano?
15 What news was in the letter to Antonio?

A Midsummer Night's Dream
1 What did Hermia's father want her to do?
2 Who was in love with Demetrius?
3 Why did Oberon and Titania quarrel? (Because . . .)
4 What did Oberon send Puck to get?
5 Where did Titania sleep?
6 What did Puck do to Bottom?
7 Who fell in love with Bottom?
8 Into whose eyes did Puck first pour the liquid?
9 What did the liquid do to both Lysander and Demetrius?
10 Why did Titania stop loving Bottom?
11 Why did Demetrius, Lysander, Helena and Hermia fall asleep?
12 Who loved who when they woke up?

Hamlet
1 Who were Hamlet's father and mother?
2 Who was Horatio?
3 Whose ghost had been seen?
4 What did the ghost tell Hamlet to do?
5 Who was Ophelia?
6 What had the players come to do?
7 Why couldn't Claudius bear the play?
8 Where was Polonius in the queen's room?
9 What happened to Polonius?
10 When the ghost appeared, who couldn't see it?
11 How did Hamlet return to Denmark?
12 What did Hamlet and Laertes do in Ophelia's grave?
13 How did the queen die?
14 What happened to Hamlet in the end?

Julius Caesar
1 Who was Julius Caesar's closest friend?
2 What did Brutus decide?
3 Who else did Cassius want to kill?
4 What advice did the wise men give to Caesar?
5 Why did Decius go to see Caesar?
6 Who struck Caesar first?
7 What promise did Antony make to the dead Caesar?
8 Why did the people stay to listen to Antony?
9 What was the paper Antony showed to the crowd?
10 Where did the two armies meet?
11 Who died first, Brutus or Cassius?
12 Why was Brutus "the noblest Roman of them all"?

Questions on the whole book

These are harder questions. Read the Introduction, and think hard about the questions before you answer them. Some of them ask for your opinion, and there is no fixed answer.

1 In *The Merchant of Venice*, what is the happy ending for each of these?
   a Antonio; *b* Bassanio; *c* Portia; *d* Gratiano; *e* Nerissa

2 In *The Merchant of Venice*, which character do you like best? Give an example to show why you like that person?

3 In *A Midsummer Night's Dream*, what do you think Bottom told his friends when they all met again?

4 In *A Midsummer Night's Dream*, which character do you like best? Give an example to show why you like that person.

5 In *Hamlet*, death comes to:
   a Polonius; *b* Ophelia; *c* Queen Gertrude; *d* Claudius;
   e Laertes; *f* Hamlet.
   1 Which of these, in your opinion, deserved to die, and why?
   2 Whose death is the saddest in the story? How did it happen?
   3 It is Hamlet's death that makes the play a tragedy. Can you explain why this is so? (The Introduction may help you.)

6 In *Julius Caesar*, it is Brutus's death that makes the play a tragedy. Can you explain why this is so?

7 Here is one important remark from each of the stories. Find the words (don't try to do the work with your books closed), and answer the questions.
   a (*The Merchant of Venice*) "Mercy falls like the gentle rain from the sky upon the earth."
      1 Whose words are they?
      2 Where were they spoken?
      3 Who were they spoken to?
      4 Why did the speaker talk about mercy?
   b (*A Midsummer Night's Dream*) "I know a bank that is covered with sweet-smelling flowers."
      1 Who says this?
      2 What usually happens on the bank?
      3 What did the speaker do at the flowery bank?
      4 What was the result of the speaker's action?
   c (*Hamlet*) "What I have done is almost as bad a thing as killing a king and marrying his brother."
      1 Who is the speaker?
      2 Who were the words spoken to?
      3 Did the person spoken to really kill a king? If not, why were the words spoken?
      4 Who married the king's brother?
   d (*Julius Caesar*) "Oh, forgive me, Caesar, for being so gentle to the men who killed you."
      1 Who is the speaker?
      2 Name three of the men who killed Caesar.
      3 What had the speaker gained by being "gentle"?
      4 In what way was he not "gentle" later on?

New words

borrow
be allowed by the owner to take and use something of his or hers, returning it later

century
a hundred years. The **sixteenth century** means the years 1501–1600.

character
(1) a person in a play (2) the special nature of a particular person, causing him or her to behave in his or her own way

ducat
a gold coin used in Venice

duel
a fight arranged between two men to settle a quarrel

flesh
the meat-like part of the body

ghost
a person who is dead but who appears again

lend
allow someone to borrow

mercy
readiness to forgive, or not to be unkind

pirate
a seaman who, with others, attacks and robs ships

Senate
the meeting of the men who ruled Rome

will
a paper written to say who must have a person's money and other things after his or her death